Marshall Pickering
An imprint of HarperCollins Publishers Ltd,
77 – 85 Fulham Palace Road, Hammersmith, London W6 8JB, UK
Reprinted 1986, 1988, 1990, 1991

First published by Marshall Morgan & Scott in 1986

British Library Cataloguing in Publication Data
Butterworth, Nick
The Precious Pearl
1. Pearl of great price (Parable) – Juvenile literature
2. Bible stories, English N.T.
I. Title II. Inkpen, Mick
226′ .809505 BT378.P4
ISBN 0-551-01278-1

Printed & bound in Italy
by L.E.G.O., Vicenza

The Precious Pearl

Nick Butterworth and Mick Inkpen

MARSHALL PICKERING

Here is a man who buys and
sells things.
He is called a merchant.
He has a fine fur coat and a
felt hat with a floppy feather.
It is his favourite.

The house he lives in is huge.
It has five floors and a fishpond
with a fountain in the front
garden.

The merchant has everything
he wants.
He has fifteen rooms filled
with furniture.

He has four freezers
full of food.
(And three fridges
for fizzy drinks.)

And there is more money under
his mattress than you could
ever imagine. Much more.
Yes, the merchant has everything
he wants, until . . .

One day, in a shop window, he sees
something. Something special.
It is a wonderful white pearl.

'Five hundred thousand pounds,' says the man in the shop.
It is even more money than the merchant has under his mattress.
But he wants that pearl more than anything in the world.

He hurries home. He has a plan.
He sells his furniture, his fridges
and his freezers full of food.
He sells his house, his fountain
and his fishpond.

He sells his fine fur coat.
But the felt hat with the
floppy feather, he keeps.
It is his favourite.

He borrows a barrow and
bundles in the money.
Off to the shop he trundles
to buy the pearl.

Oh dear! He is still six pounds short.
'Sell me your hat for six pounds,' says the man in the shop.
The merchant laughs.
He hands the man his hat and takes the pearl.

Hooray! The pearl is his at last.
Jesus says, 'God is like the
merchant's pearl.
It costs everything to know him.
But he is worth more than
anything in the world.'